FLORA IN FOCUS

CACTI
THE FLOWERING DESERT

SMITHMARK

For this English language edition:
Todtri Productions Ltd., New York

This edition published in 1996 by SMITHMARK
Publishers, a division of U.S. Media Holdings,
Inc., 16 East 32nd Street, New York, NY 10016.

SMITHMARK books are available for bulk pur-
chase for sales promotion and premium use. For
details write or call the manager of special sales,
SMITHMARK Publishers, 16 East 32nd Street,
New York, NY 10016; (212) 532-6600.

Editions of this book will appear simultaneously
in France, Germany, Great Britain, Italy and
the Netherlands under auspices of Euredition bv,
Den Haag, Netherlands

Photographs:
PPWW Plant Pictures World Wide, Daan Smit
Text:
Nicky den Hartogh
Translation:
Tony Langham
Concept, design and editing:
Boris van Dobbenburgh
Typesetting:
Mark Dolk/Peter Verwey Grafische Produkties
Color separation:
Unifoto PTY LTD, Cape Town
Production:
Agora United Graphic Services bv, 's-Graveland
Printing and binding:
Egedsa, Sabadell, Spain

ISBN 0-8317-6121-0

INTRODUCTION

Centuries pass: the shape of the earth changes. But unchanging in time, like the clouds passing over it, there is a powerful genus of plants living on the distant mountains of America: the cacti. Like gigantic runes from the grey mists of time they weather the storms of the ages; conflict and hardship are their lot; determination and a tough life force, their weapons. (When the eternal winds buffet all around, it is as though the immortal melody of Beethoven whispers softly all around them.)

(FROM CURT BACKEBERG, *THE HUNT FOR CACTI FROM TEXAS TO PATAGONIA*, KOSMOS N.V., AMSTERDAM, 1932)

Cacti are a curious family. After centuries of familiarization they no longer arouse the astonishment that they used to, either in Europe or in other parts of the world. Nevertheless, they are certainly no ordinary plants. They are so far removed from "common leafy plants" that their characteristic structure and particular development and the extreme environment in which they are found has inspired many people to become lifelong collectors. By no means everyone finds these inaccessible, stiff and thorny plants which stand in pots on the windowsill equally charming, but anyone who has seen cacti in their natural habitat is at least intrigued.

Farmers in America, Africa and Australia view cacti as troublesome weeds. For the people of the South American mountains the fruit of the gigantic cactus, whose mighty pillars are silhouetted against the slopes, was once an essential part of their diet. The creatures of the desert depend on the cactus for their survival. A small owl finds a safe haven there; the pigeon collects the nectar in the cactus flower. On the edge of the jungle the queen of the night opens its magical flowers at dusk to entice moths. A spherical cactus, taller than a man, stands alone on a pitiless, bare, rocky plateau. Small cacti are concealed between the fissures in the rock, sometimes in clusters with many heads. Large, bush-shaped specimens with formidable thorns are used to form impenetrable hedges around courtyards.

In their countries of origin, some cacti can live for hundreds of years. Following a long life in which they have conquered many dangers, the pillar-shaped giants of the family can reach heights of thirty to sixty feet. A large, spherical barrel cactus can weigh a ton or more and evaporates several thousand times less water than an "ordinary" plant of the same weight. It is often said that cacti are experts in the art of survival, and this is very true. They grow in places where other plants would die. In the course of their development they have succeeded in adapting to extreme drought, and the capacity to form leaves eventually disappeared altogether. The functions of the leaves were taken over by the other green parts of the plant. When there has been no rainfall for a long time, the cacti are in a sort of state of hibernation, reducing all the life processes to an absolute minimum. Some species even withdraw into the earth for protection, and apparently lifeless, wait for better times. When the rain comes at last, the delicate network of roots just below the surface acts like a huge sponge, in a short time soaking up every last drop of rainwater. Cacti are like living reservoirs of water. The moisture is stored in the body of the plant and carefully protected against evaporation.

The stomata in the skin are deep, and placed a long way apart, and the surface of the cactus is covered in a layer of wax to restrict the loss of moisture into the atmosphere. Many members of the cactus family have armed themselves against the hostile outside world with sharp thorns, a dense cover of hair, or an armored skin. Plants which can survive long, dry periods by storing water and using it very economically, are known by the collective name, "succulents"; they tend to share a rather fleshy appearance. The word "succulentis" actually means "rich in juice." Succulents are found in arid regions throughout the world and can belong to totally different families. A special characteristic of the cactus family is the fact that (almost) all the members are succulents.

The cactus family originates from America. Cacti which are apparently indigenous to the south of Europe, Africa, Australia or Asia have been introduced there by man for various reasons. In some cases the introduction of these spiny plants had catastrophic results, as for example, in Australia, where huge areas of land were overrun with Opuntia. When even strong, toxic herbicides proved incapable of stopping the spread of these plants, the cactus moth was used to combat them. These insects bore holes in the body of the plant so that the cactus be-

comes susceptible to destructive viruses.
Some mistletoe cacti (Rhipsalis varieties) are indigenous in tropical Africa and on the islands of Ceylon and Madagascar, but botanists suspect that they developed there from seeds carried by birds from America.

The flower of the saguaro (Carnegia gigantea) is the symbol of the state of Arizona in the southwest of the United States. The coat-of-arms of Mexico contains a prickly pear (Opuntia) on which a golden eagle has landed with a snake in its beak. The greatest number of cacti are found in the Mexican steppes, plateaus and deserts with the adjacent southwestern United States. A large number of the more than two thousand varieties are indigenous in Mexico. The impressive, tree-shaped specimens with branches are characteristic of these hot, dusty regions, as are the bushy varieties and magnificent tall columnar cacti. Miniature varieties, often only few inches tall, lie hidden and are frequently difficult to find, even for experienced botanists.

About half of Mexico is dominated by a desert climate with an average rainfall of less than nine inches per year. The cactus was ascribed a magical/religious significance by the pre-Colombian people who lived in the country before the Spanish conquerors started their invasions of destruction. Even after centuries of suppression, this still plays a role. The ceremonial use of peyote - which was called the "Devil's root" by missionaries - has even spread in the last century to parts of America, where this particular cactus is not even found.

Not long after the Spanish discovered cacti in the "New World," the plants were shipped back to Europe. They became fashionable among the aristocracy. They were cultivated and became quite common where the climate allowed. From time to time interest in cacti in Europe would diminish, and then they would become extremely popular again. When the cultivation of succulents became all the rage at the end of the nineteenth and the beginning of the twentieth century, cacti were sought after on a large scale for trading purposes. Eventually, the survival of some species was threatened to such a large extent, especially in Mexico, that they had to be protected by law. As cultivated seedlings generally thrive better than imported specimens, modern growers generally cultivate cacti from seed.

In the United States, the natural habitat of the cactus family stretches far into the north. Some Opuntia are even found in Canada at fifty degrees latitude, and therefore require little heat.

However, compared with the rich variety of cactus flora in the south of the United States, Mexico and several other Central American countries, there are very few different varieties further north. In South America, cacti are found as far south as the inhospitable regions of Patagonia, the "tail" of Argentina. The mountains of northern Argentina and the adjacent southern part of Bolivia are particularly rich in different varieties. These include the gigantic Helianthocereus pasacana, a columnar cactus, the thick, woody stems of which are used as firewood and timber for furniture and doors. The sweet, edible fruits are the size of a tennis ball, and are sold under the name "pasacana."

Quite a few varieties and species of cactus have a very limited natural habitat. There are some varieties which can only be found in one place, particularly in mountain valleys which are more or less shut off from the outside world. Lobivia, Parodia and the dwarf genus Rebutia grow in Peru and Bolivia up to the snowline in the high mountain regions at heights of 10,000 or 13,000 feet, where they endure extreme heat in the day and frost at night.

To the north and south of the equator the infinite jungles stretch from Central America across a large part of South America. This is the home of the forest cacti. The strap cactus (Epiphyllum), Christmas cactus (Schlumbergera), mistletoe cactus (Rhipsalis), Queen of the Night (Hylocereus) and moon cactus (Selenicereus) spread their long, snake-like, leaf-shaped, articulated and cylindrical stems over rocks, climbing up the trunks and branches of neighboring plants and rooting high up above the ground in the forks of trees. As the humidity is high, the forest cacti do not have to be so economical with water as their relatives in drier regions, and they are often unarmed with spines.

(In America the cactus has also become increasingly widespread as a result of human intervention; thus it is not always clear whether the plants are actually indigenous in a particular area.)

The large cacti are often the most striking living organisms in deserts and semi-deserts because of their bizarre shapes and impressive size, and yet they are by no means alone. They live side by side with a large number of reptiles, insects, birds and mammals which have adapted to the climatological conditions, just like the cactus: the lack of rainfall, the heat, the extreme drop in temperatures at night, the periods of frost. No matter how effectively a cactus has armed itself with thorns to protect its juicy body from being devoured and from other dangers, there are always some creatures which manage to break through the armor. Like the cactus itself, they have also learned to survive in arid regions. The gigantic columnar cactus (Carnegia gigantea) grows in the Sonora desert, a huge area which covers a large part of Mexico, as well as part of Arizona in the United States. In America, this giant is known as saguaro. When it is young, a small saguaro is in great danger of being devoured by hungry rodents, and even if it manages to reach the age of twenty-five undamaged - when the plant is still only twelve inches tall - it is still at risk. Once the mature saguaro towers over the surrounding area the hawk will build its nest in the forks of its raised arms. The Gila woodpecker can hammer round the thorns with its long beak until they fall off, making a space where a hole can be pecked out. At night the red lynx climbs up to search for the woodpecker's eggs, apparently unperturbed by the sharp thorns. The flowers are fertilized by a pigeon which later eats the fruit. The pulp of the fruit rots away, but the seeds remain undamaged and leave the bird's intestinal tract at the other end. (The seeds of a cactus with fleshy fruit are often dispersed over a much larger area than those of cacti with dry fruit, because the seed remains where it has fallen, or has been carried by the wind or water.)

Even in the so-called saguaro forests - part of which have been designated as a nature reserve - cacti do not usually stand close together - the density of plants in arid regions is determined by the amount of water available. This is also used by other plants: grasses, annual herbs, shrubs and small trees with small leaves, such as the mesquite (Prosopis juliflora), the creosote shrub (Larrea divaricata) and the bizarre boojum tree (Idria columnaris). Like the cactus, the annuals devote a great deal of energy to the development of flowers and seed. Countless seeds wait for rain, well protected against drying out. As soon as a shower has fallen on the parched ground, small plants germinate everywhere, and are soon covered in flowers. When this happens, it is said that the desert blossoms.

CEREUS PERUVIANUS

Although the members of the cactus family have a large number of characteristics in common, there is a great deal of variation in their appearance. In the first place, the differences in the way that spherical, segmented and columnar cacti grow are very striking. A columnar cactus such as Cereus peruvianus develops vertical columns with pronounced ribs, which enable the body of the cactus to contract and expand as the supply of moisture decreases and increases.

OPUNTIA TUNA

As regards its structure, Opuntia, the prickly pear, is completely different from columnar cacti. The plant consists of a number of broad, flat segments, and when it has flowered, the fleshy fruit appear on these segments. The flowers of Opuntia tuna, a shrub-like, segmented cactus from Jamaica, are a bright red color.

CEREUS PERUVIANUS "MONSTROSUS"

Cereus peruvianus branches out from the foot into a number of vertical or diagonal, slender spreading columns, together forming a plant which can be sixteen feet wide and more than ten feet tall. Normally every column has a number of parallel ribs running lengthways. However, in Cereus peruvianus "Monstrosus," the rock cactus, they are interrupted by transverse grooves, so that irregular, knobbly growths form on the branches. This gives the cactus a rather curious appearance which greatly appeals to collectors.

All sorts of different types of cacti, varying from spherical to columnar cacti, have been collected together in the Desert Botanical Garden in Phoenix, Arizona: (in the foreground, there are examples of Echinocactus and Ferocactus), a prickly pear (extreme left: Opuntia), and shrub-like cacti (center: Myrtillocactus), as well as tall, columnar species (background: Carnegia).

E CHINOPSIS MAMILLOSA
Improbably large, fragrant flowers appear at the top of the small, more or less spherical bodies of Echinopsis mamillosa, the false porcupine cactus from Bolivia.

NEOBUXBAUMIA POLYLOPHA "CRISTATA"

In some parts of Mexico the imposing columns of Neobuxbaumia form forests on the slopes. Between the dignified vertical trunks of a cactus forest there will always be one which does not reach up, but instead grows out to form a wide fan which stands out like a magnificent sculptured ornament. This sort of growth is known as a "cristate." Cristate forms occur in several cactus varieties. They are very popular, and were greatly sought after by the collectors who used to travel round cactus areas. Now that the removal and exportation of these wonderful specimens is prohibited, young cristate forms are cultivated only from parent plants which were themselves cultivated. The specimen illustrated here is in the Jardin Exotique in Monaco.

MAMMILLARIA BOCASANA

The small, spherical plant bodies of Mammillaria bocasana are tightly packed together in compact groups. They are surrounded by a downy white haze of silky-soft, shiny hairs. The characteristic long red fruits are every bit as striking as the flowers. Underneath the dense cover of hair, there are numerous knobs (tubercles) which give Mammillaria its name (mammilla means "nipple").

MAMMILLARIA NEJAPENSIS
The nipple-shaped swellings, covered in a crown of thorns and felt, form a beautiful pattern interrupted by a striking ring of flowers. The way in which the flowers are arranged in rings, appearing on very young plants, is characteristic of many Mammillaria varieties.

MAMMILLARIA SPINOSISSIMA
Together with the prickly pear (Opuntia), the pincushion cactus (Mammillaria) is a very large genus in the cactus family. Most of the species are indigenous to Mexico. Many pincushion cacti have a milky-white juice which flows from the wound when the body of the cactus is damaged. Often the plants develop in many-headed groups, covered with attractive rings of flowers and colorful fruits which increase its ornamental value, as does the covering of delicate thorns.

L EUCHTENBERGIA PRINCIPIS
Place of origin: central and northern Mexico.

A RROJODOA MULTIFLORA
Place of origin: northern Brazil

H AMATOCACTUS SETISPINUS
Place of origin: southern
United States and northern Mexico

NOPALEA COCHENILLIFERA

The cochineal cactus (Nopalea cochenillifera) has been cultivated for such a long time that it is no longer possible to find out where exactly it originated. Like Opuntia, the prickly pear, to which Nopalea is closely related, the plant was cultivated in countries with a mild climate, as a host plant for the cochineal louse, a parasite which was used in the past as a source of red dye.

OPUNTIA INERMIS

There are more than two hundred different Opuntia varieties. It is found from Canada in the north to Argentina in the south. Thus it is hardly surprising that there are big differences between the various species. There are low, creeping plants with segments which are less than an inch across, but there are also large, tree-shaped Opuntias which can grow to a height of thirteen feet or more, and form a woody trunk at the foot. Nevertheless, most varieties are easy to identify because of their characteristic segments.

RITTEROCEREUS PRUINOSUS

The many-armed crown of Ritterocereus pruinosus, a columnar cactus from Central Mexico, reaches a height of twenty-three feet.

ECHINOCEREUS DELAETII

The long white hairs (which are actually soft thorns) mean that Echinocereus delaetii, a hairy dwarf cactus, looks like a smaller version of the better known old-man cactus (Cephalocereus senilis). The columns grow to a maximum height of twelve inches and have flowers with a diameter of two and a half inches.

Members of the cactus family which have a plant body in the shape of a column are described by the collective term, columnar cactus, no matter how small the columns, and even if they are not absolutely vertical, as in the case of many of the larger varieties. In the past, all the columnar cacti were classified in the Cereus genus. This is no longer the case, but the word cereus (which means "candle") is still found in the contemporary names: Ritterocereus, Echinocereus, Cephalocereus, Trichocereus and so on.

E CHINOCEREUS ALBATUS

E CHINOCEREUS PENTALOPHUS
Echinocereus, a dwarf columnar cactus, is indigenous to Mexico and the southwest of the United States.
The flower is the symbol of the state of New Mexico. There are approximately sixty-five varieties, predominantly low-growing plants with small vertical or horizontal columns. After a while they usually develop larger or smaller groups by means of runners. Some species take on the color of their surroundings and are hardly visible against the background. However, when they flower, all the attention is focused on the charming flowers, which are relatively large and have striking colors. The fruits of various dwarf columnar cacti can be used for making jams and jellies.

◄

E CHINOCEREUS DUBIUS

E CHINOCEREUS PAPILLOSUS

RHIPSALIS MESEMBRYANTHEMOIDES
The transparent berries of Rhipsalis mesembry-anthemoides attract more attention than the small flowers from which they spring. The majority of Rhipsalis varieties originated in the South American (mainly Brazilian) jungle. They wind round branches, hang down from the forks of trees, or grow in narrow fissures in rocks, stretching their long, segmented stems over the rock. Some varieties have thin, cylindrical, rod-like branches. Rhipsalis is also known as the mistletoe cactus. Apart from a few exceptions, the plants do not have thorns.
The white, red or purple berries are eaten by birds, so that the seeds are dispersed far and wide. Perhaps this is how the seed was transported from America in the dim and distant past to tropical Africa, Ceylon and Madagascar, where Rhipsalis is now included amongst the indigenous flora.

PSEUDORHIPSALIS MACRANTHA ▶

RHIPSALIS SPECIES
Some Rhipsalis species have flat, leafy, segmented stems.

SELENICEREUS MACDONALDIAE

Selenicereus, the moon Cereus, is a night-flowering plant. The large flowers, between seven to sixteen inches long, are so beautiful that some of the species were given fairytale names such as the "Queen of the Night" and "Princess of the Night." They open when the sun has set and disperse a sweet fragrance, attracting nocturnal animals which pollinate them. By early morning the flowers have withered. The natural habitat of the moon Cereus stretches from Mexico in the north to Colombia in the south. The plants are not very striking until they flower. They root in the layer of humus in the forks of tree branches, or creep between rocks and fissures. In many cases the long, snake-like sections have aerial roots. The juice of Selenicereus grandiflorus is used as a medicine for the treatment of heart disease. In the past, botanical gardens would open their conservatories on the night that the magnificent flowers of the "Queen of the Night" bloomed. In America, so-called "moonlight visits" are still organized in cactus gardens, so that the beauty of these nocturnal flowers does not go unnoticed.

TRICHOCEREUS PACHENOI

Many columnar cacti also have a magical appearance when they blossom. Trichocereus pachenoi from Ecuador is more or less tree-shaped, with many branches and flowers that can be more than eight inches long.

HELIOCEREUS SPECIOSUS VAR.
HAMECAMENSIS

HELIOCEREUS SPECIOSUS VAR.
HAMECAMENSIS

HELIOCEREUS SPECIOSUS

In contrast with the moon Cereus (Selinicereus), the sun Cereus (Heliocereus) flowers in the daytime.
The natural habitat of the sun Cereus is in Mexico, south of Mexico City. Crimson flowers, six inches long and up to four inches wide, appear on the slender, flexible stems and remain open for several days.

Heliocereus speciosus var. Amecamensis has white flowers. The sun Cereus flowers easily. It is suitable as a pot plant, and is crossed with related cacti by growers to create new varieties.

DENDROCEREUS NUDIFLORUS
The fresh, green, winged young shoots on the tree-shaped Dendrocereus, which can grow to a height of thirty-three feet. It originates only from Cuba.

DEAMIA TESTUDO
Deamia testudo is indigenous in the area which stretches from Mexico in the north to Colombia in the south. The cactus clings to stones, branches and trunks and can climb up into trees with the help of aerial roots. It is difficult to imagine that a plant with such a fiercely prickly appearance could produce such fairytale-like flowers. They are yellow or white and can grow to a diameter of eight inches.

HELIABRAVOA CHENDE
Heliabravoa develops into an impressive tree. The crown reaches a height of twenty-three feet and has approximately the same width.

CALYMANTHIUM SUBSTERILE
With a height of twenty-six feet, this cactus from the north of Peru is also one of the tallest in the family.

OPUNTIA
TOMENTOSA

OPUNTIA FICUS-INDICA

Since time immemorial, this cactus has been one of the most important sources of food for the native people in their indigenous habitat. The fruit of various species is edible. The prickly pear is eaten as a salad. Candied slices of various spherical cacti are eaten as a delicacy, and the moisture in the cactus is used for beverages. Nowadays, very few people depend on the cactus to survive, but for many people, certain products form part of the diet. The fruit of Opuntia ficus-indica, the edible prickly pear, is sold throughout the world. This bushy, sometimes tree-shaped cactus, is cultivated on a large scale in subtropical and tropical regions. Israel, Morocco, Italy and Spain are the most important producers. The ocher or red fruit are sold as cactus fruit or desert fig. Desert figs are rich in vitamins, and contain a refreshing, juicy pulp.

Peeling the fruit is quite a skill. The sharp thorns are removed when the fruit is harvested, but usually, numerous little thorns (glochids) are left behind. These can irritate the skin and sometimes cause inflammation, so that it is important to rub the skin of the fruit carefully with a cloth or brush, and rinse it under the tap.

AUSTROCYLINDROPUNTIA SUBULATA

Following a long process of development, after which they eventually attained the maximum degree of succulence, many members of the cactus family have lost all trace of leaf formation. However, some cacti do have rudimentary leaves. The awl-shaped green protuberances accompanying the sharp thorns of Austrocylindropuntia are actually greatly reduced leaves. They are superfluous for the cactus, because the function of the leaves (to convert nutrients and exchange gases) is taken over by other green parts of the plant.

TRICHOCEREUS BRIDGESII

The long, colored thorns are one of the charming features of Trichocereus bridgesii from Brazil. The beautiful flowers with a scent like jasmine only appear after many years, and open at night.

CEREUS PERUVIANUS

Columnar cactus in the Jardin Exotique, Monaco.

OPUNTIA SETISPINA

Setispina means "with many thorns."

BORZICACTUS AUREISPINA
Country of origin: Brazil.

E RDISIA TENUICULA
Country of origin: Peru.

B ORZICACTUS SAMAIPATANUS
Country of origin: Bolivia.

PILOSOCEREUS PALMERI

Usually there is a long period of preparation before a cactus finally flowers, often spectacularly, but very briefly. In Pilosocereus palmeri, a large branched columnar cactus from Mexico, it is clear a long time in advance where the flowers will appear.

Tight, woolly clumps appear over the entire flowering area on the ribs. After the bud hesitantly appears in the woolly nest, it still takes a long time to develop and for the delicate petals to unfold.

RHODOCACTUS GRANDIFOLIUS

Some members of the cactus family look like "ordinary" shrubs or small trees. They have trunks, branches and leaves. They do not have leafy segmented stems, like the Christmas cactus or the leaf-stalk cactus, but true leaves which can be up to six inches long. Some of these plants include the "rose cactus" (Rhodocactus grandifolius) and the Barbados berry (Pereskia aculeata). These are sometimes seen as the oldest forms of modern cacti, and seem to prove that the thorny succulents have evolved from ordinary leafy plants. During a drought the rose cactus sheds its leaves to restrict evaporation. Most cacti have adapted in a more far-reaching way and actually bear very little resemblance to "ordinary" plants.

SCHLUMBERGERA TRUNCATA HYBRID

One of the most popular pot plants in the cactus family is the profusely flowering Christmas cactus.

Schlumbergera truncata (synonym: Zygocactus truncatus) is the parent plant of many hybrids found in living rooms, and is therefore the most important species.

In its natural habitat the plant is epiphytic (plants which live in trees) in the forests of the Organ mountains in the state of Rio de Janiero in Brazil. Like most other forest cacti, the Christmas cactus has a very different life cycle from other members of the family. When it is cultivated it also requires high humidity and light, moist soil, rich in humus.

EPIPHYLLUM HYBRID

Leaf-stalk cacti (Epiphyllum varieties) originate from the tropical regions of Central and South America. Like bromelias, ferns and orchids, they are epiphytic plants and live in the trees of the rainforests. The long branches, consisting of leaf-like segments, do not normally have any thorns, which is characteristic of forest cacti.

True Epiphyllum varieties bloom at night.

Numerous hybrids have been cultivated by crossing Epiphyllum varieties with other cacti, including large, flowered Cereus varieties, Heliocereus and Selenicereus. The hybrids have extremely beautiful, large flowers in every shade, from white to yellow to a purplish pink. Although they can differ in color and shape, the characteristic slender style protruding from the clump of stamens, can almost always be identified immediately.

◄

When the rain comes at last after a long period of drought, it is usually short but very heavy, and the desert springs to life. A cactus is able to absorb large quantities of water immediately because of the spreading network of roots just below the surface, and then stores the water in its fleshy body. In some species the thickened roots serve to hold water, as well as the parts of the cactus that are above ground. The rainfall does not only result in changes in cacti. After a good downpour, shrubs are suddenly covered with leaves, and all sorts of herb-like plants spring up from seeds and soon start to flower. The arid desert and the steppe vegetation are transformed into a meadow of flowers.

OPUNTIA PHAEACANTHA

OPUNTIA PHAEACANTHA
The rocks in the desert landscape in the extreme south of
Arizona on the Mexican border are
eroded into fascinating shapes as a
result of sandstorms and heavy
downpours. A prickly pear has
managed to cling to the slope in the
arid soil at the edge of the road.
◀

OPUNTIA
An elegant gate decorated with an Opuntia motif is the entrance to the cactus garden in the Botanical Gardens of Singapore.

AUSTROCYLINDROPUNTIA SUBULATA
Place of origin: Southern Peru.

OPUNTIA TOMENTOSA
Several prickly pears can develop over the years into tree-like specimens, six to seven feet tall. Gradually the lower segments form a cylindrical trunk which eventually becomes woody.
Opuntia tomentosa ultimately reaches a height of twenty feet. It has a trunk about a foot long. When it has flowered, sweet red fruits appear on the edges of the segments, where there are no thorns, as on the trunk at the foot. The plant originates from the plateaus in Mexico, but was introduced and has become indigenous in other hot areas.

LOPHOPHORA WILLIAMSII

The small, soft, fleshy peyote grows only on the stony, loamy soil in the deserts of northern Mexico and southern Texas. The plant has been closely related to the lifestyle of the various Indian tribes who have inhabited this area for more than two thousand, perhaps even three thousand years. The body of the plant of the peyote contains the substance mescaline. Mescaline can produce colorful visions, and appears to give the user an all-encompassing sense of oneness with creation. Both collecting this cactus and its use are accompanied by ceremonies which are centuries old. The peyote is used by the Huichol in Mexico, amongst others. Traditionally the first specimens found in the perfect places after a long trip, are "caught" with great care and respect. The prize is not intended solely for personal use, but is also traded with neighboring tribes. In the course of this century, the cult of the cactus has spread into the United States - much further north than the natural habitat of peyote - and has a special place in the Native American Church, which combines Christian Faith with peyote use.

CONSOLEA SPINOSISSIMA

Consolea spinosissima from Jamaica can grow to a height of twenty feet and has a trunk approximately eight inches thick. It is armed with numerous long, sharp spines.

CONSOLEA MONILIFORMIS
The tips of the tree-like Consolea look rather like the segments of Opuntia, but are longer, less thick and with a more irregular circumference.

CLEISTOCACTUS STRAUSII

◀

CLEISTOCACTUS STRAUSII "CRISTATA"
Hairy cristate of Cleistocactus strausii.

CLEISTOCACTUS STRAUSII "CRISTATA"
Hairy cristate of Cleistocactus strausii.

E CHINOCEREUS TRIGLOCHIDATUS
Place of origin: Arizona, western Texas
and southern Colorado.

E CHINOCEREUS ENGELMANNII
Place of origin: desert regions of
Arizona, California and Mexico.
◀

F EROCACTUS ACANTHODES
Place of origin: Mexico and
the southwest of the United
States (Sonora desert, Baja,
California).

OPUNTIA FICUS-INDICA

Cochineal insect on the segments of the edible prickly pear. A number of Opuntia varieties have become very common in tropical and subtropical regions as a result of their commercial use. In quite a few cases the introduction of Opuntia into other parts of the world resulted in total disaster. As soon as the plants felt at home in the new country, they soon took over altogether. Pieces of the Opuntia plant break off easily, and can take root in the most improbable places. In Australia in particular, huge areas were overrun by these spiny plants.

In the east, Opuntias were planted because the cochineal insect is a a parasite which lives on the segments.

Even before the Europeans settled in America, the Indians had used these insects to produce a beautiful crimson dye with which they dyed the garments of high-ranking people. The production was taken over by the Spanish, who imposed stringent measures to retain a monopoly on the profitable trade in cochineal for more than two centuries. In the end they lost this monopoly, and the cochineal cactus was cultivated in various countries until the market completely collapsed because the valuable crimson dye could be prepared by chemical means.

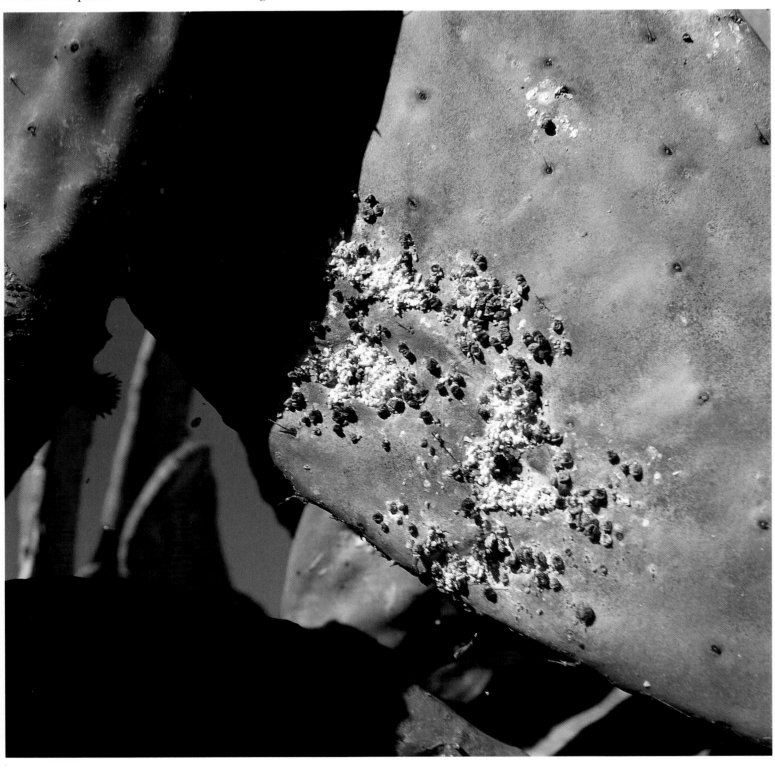

O PUNTIA
GOSSELINIANA

O PUNTIA
Cacti are able to survive in climatological conditions which vary markedly
in their natural environment. After
months of drought, heavy downpours
can produce raging torrents. After the
heat of the day, the temperatures in
desert regions at night sometimes drop
sharply, and may even fall below freezing
point.

CYLINDROPUNTIA SPINOSIOR

Like Opuntia (the prickly pear), Cylindropuntia has large flowers which open wide. The plants are so closely related that many botanists classify them in the same genus. However, this relationship is not apparent in the structure of the plants. In place of the flat segments, Cylindropuntia has cylindrical branches, which explains its scientific name. This cactus is sometimes known as the sheath-fig cactus because the thorns are surrounded by a membranous sheath.

CYLINDROPUNTIA SPINOSIOR

CYLINDROPUNTIA VERSICOLOR

Cylindropuntia versicolor, which is indigenous to Arizona and northern Mexico, can ultimately attain a height of thirteen feet.

The slender trunks are sometimes used as fuel by the native inhabitants of the region.

CYLINDROPUNTIA VERSICOLOR

O PUNTIA BASILARIS

Opuntia basilaris, a low-growing prickly pear, grows in the desert and steppe regions in the north of Mexico, and the adjacent southwest of the United States. The broad segments of the stem are stiffly lined up, and harmonize with the surrounding grasses and rocks because of their special coloring. The flowers develop along the edges of the segments which formed at the beginning of the year. They are large in relation to the size of the cactus, and spread out. There is a ring of many stamens in the heart of the flower; the stamens bend into the center towards the thick stigma as soon as an insect touches them, to cover the pistil with pollen. After fertilization, the receptacle develops into a dry fruit containing large, fat seeds. Opuntia basilaris does not have any real thorns. On the other hand, the plant does have large numbers of "glochids," minuscule thorns which are hardly visible, but can easily penetrate the skin, causing itching and inflammation. These little thorns, like the segmented forms and wide, spreading flowers are characteristic of Opuntias.

OPUNTIA ACICULATA/OPUNTIA MICRODASYS
Landscape in the southwest of the United States, where the large columnar cactus rises up amongst the open undergrowth. In the foreground there are two prickly pears: Opuntia aciculata (left) and Opuntia microdasys (right). Microdasys means "with small brushes."

These brushes consist of treacherously small thorns which can damage the eyes of cattle, and have given Opuntia microdasys the reputation for blinding creatures.

O PUNTIA ACICULATA

O PUNTIA MICRODASYS

O PUNTIA PHAEACANTHA

O PUNTIA HUMIFUSA

CYLINDROPUNTIA BIGELOWII
The flower of Cylindropuntia bigelowii can vary in color from white to yellowish-green or bronze.

CYLINDROPUNTIA BIGELOWII

From a distance the teddy-bear cholla, as this cactus is known in America, looks fairly harmless, but the merest touch, and the treacherous thorns work their way into the skin. They have small hooks, which means that it is no easy matter to get them out again.

CYLINDROPUNTIA BIGELOWII

OPUNTIA GOSSELINIANA VAR. SANTA-RITA
This prickly pear in the mountains of Santa-Rita
(southeast Arizona) naturally has a purplish-pink hue.

ECHINOCEREUS TRIGLOCHIDATUS
Whole colonies of dwarf columnar cacti are concealed in fissures in rocks. Their presence is betrayed only by the bright colors of the flowers.

Mimicry, a phenomenon by which plants adapt their color and growth in such a way that they are virtually invisible against the background, occurs occasionally in the cactus family. Entirely bare rocks and stony ground sometimes quite unexpectedly prove to harbor life when plants begin to flower.

ECHINOCEREUS
TRIGLOCHIDATUS

CARNEGIA GIGANTEA

The saguaro (Carnegia gigantea), the giant columnar cactus from American westerns and the lonely silhouette popular in cartoons, is the largest form of life to be found in the Sonora desert in Mexico, and the southwest of the United States. A mature specimen can reach a height of more than forty feet, and weighs several tons. To attain this size, the plant has to overcome countless dangers. When it is small, it is threatened by drought, floods during torrential downpours, severe frost in winter and rodents which are always on the lookout for a juicy morsel. When the giant columnar cactus reaches a height of six to eight feet after fifty to sixty years, it produces flowers for the first time in its life. At the age of seventy-five to a hundred, when the saguaro is thirteen to twenty feet tall, the huge side arms develop. These are covered in flowers after only a few years. In order to develop fruit, the flowers must be pollinated during the short time that they are open. One of the creatures which pollinates the flower of the saguaro is a pigeon which feeds on the nectar, transferring the pollen from the stamens to the pistils. The green fruit is eaten by birds and mammals. The bright red pulp is digested, and the small black seeds are dispersed far and wide in the droppings.

To remain upright, the saguaro has a strong, woody internal structure, which remains standing long after the plant has died and the fleshy part has rotted away. Tall, columnar cacti like the saguaro not only have an extensive network of roots to absorb all the moisture in the surrounding area, but also have a long tap root, which helps to anchor the plant firmly.

CARNEGIA GIGANTEA

CARNEGIA GIGANTEA

CYLINDROPUNTIA

A curious phenomenon occurs in some cactus varieties.
The fruit does not drop off when it has ripened, but stays on the plant to flower. This process repeats itself again and again, and after many years there are large bunches of fruit on the branches, as illustrated in this Cylindropuntia.

CYLINDROPUNTIA VERSICOLOR

CYLINDROPUNTIA BIGELOWII

OPUNTIA CATINGICOLA

The Catingas are situated in the northeast of Brazil, where the sea winds do not bring any rain because they have released all their moisture in the coastal regions. In these arid steppes, cacti and thornbushes form an impenetrable wilderness. This is where the Opuntia catingicola grows - a prickly pear of which the natural habitat is incorporated in the Latin name of the plant (catingicola means "in the Catinga").

OPUNTIA FICUS-INDICA
Because the edible prickly pear has been cultivated for centuries and became commonplace in regions with a favorable climate everywhere, it is no longer possible to determine precisely where the plant originated.

Landscape with saguaro or giant columnar cactus (Carnegia gigantea), organ-pipe cacti (Marshallocereus thurberi) and the pale green creosote shrub (Larrea divaricata).

MARSHALLOCEREUS THURBERI

The organ-pipe cactus branches out just above the foot in a number of vertical columns; other cacti with a similar pattern of growth are also sometimes called organ-pipe cactus in America. However, the "true" organ-pipe cactus (Marshallocereus thurberi) is found only in southern Arizona and Mexico. The creosote shrub (shown on the left), one of the few shrubs which can survive the harsh conditions of the desert, grows in the same region. The leaves are so small that they evaporate very little water. In the long dry seasons the desert shrub loses all its leaves, and sometimes dies down to the ground. As soon as there is any rain, new shoots immediately appear from the base of the plant. It is said that the creosote shrub lives even longer than the oldest tree in the world. (Its buds are eaten as capers.)

This cactus area with red rock formations is part of the Boyce Thomson Botanical Garden in the southwestern United States. ▶

THELOCACTUS SPECIES

Long, strikingly colored thorns and splendid flowers are the qualities which make Thelocactus so valuable to a cactus collector. There are almost thirty species. They originate in Mexico and Texas.

Mammillaria Species

Mammillaria Species

M AMMILLARIA COMPRESSA

Apart from the cacti, a number of desert shrubs also manage to survive in the inhospitable arid regions of the American continent. The red flowering ocolito (Fouquieria digitata) from Mexico, forms the background to several spherical, segmented and columnar cacti (including Lophocereus schottii). For part of the year the ocolito looks lifeless, with its vertical, thorny but leafless twigs, but after a good warm downpour, the plant is suddenly transformed, and within forty-eight hours the previously apparently lifeless branches are covered in leaves.

FEROCACTUS EMORYI

Ferocactus varieties can vary in shape from a purely spherical cactus to a cylinder. There is also a lot of variation in size. Ferocactus emoryi can grow to a height of almost eight feet, and about half that width. When it has flowered, the robust body of the plant is crowned with striking fruit.

FEROCACTUS

The valuable moisture of spreading colossi, such as Ferocactus and Echinocactus, have saved many a traveler in the desert from dehydration. Several quarts of water can be obtained by cutting off the top of the cactus and crushing the juicy tissue. The fleshy, juicy bodies of some varieties are cut into slices, candied and eaten as a delicacy. A number of Ferocactus varieties have large spines with a hook at the end, as does the species illustrated here. This is why the plant is known in America as the "fishhook cactus."

FEROCACTUS EMORYI ▶

LOPHOCEREUS SCHOTTII

In America the Lophocereus schottii is known as the "whisker cactus," an appropriate name, because the striking long grey bristly thorns, which mark the flowering area of this cactus, are reminiscent of whiskers. The cactus flowers at night, and forms many branches near the foot. The columns can reach a height of ten to twenty-three feet.

CYLINDROPUNTIA LEPTOCAULIS VAR. VAGINATA
The yellow thorns of this fiercely armed "sheath-fig cactus" are partly surrounded by a straw-colored cylinder. The profusion of thin branches with sharp thorns forms a dense thorny vegetation, and therefore it is not surprising that in the areas where it is indigenous - Mexico and the southwest of the United States - it is considered to be an extremely troublesome weed.

INDEX